BUS STOP

Clive Gifford

Illustrated by Louise Gardner

Bob stood by the old bus stop on Fog Lane.
He wanted to take a trip somewhere away from the rain.
Doc Box saw Bob and gave him a friendly nod.

She thought that standing at the old bus stop was odd.
No buses had stopped there for weeks and weeks.
The new bus stop was on Nut Street.

Bus STOP

Fog Lane

"Are you waiting for a car or a cab?" asked Doc Box.

"No, a **special** bus," said Bob, and Doc Box walked off.

2

Look at the different ways Bob gets around. Match each word to a picture and write it out underneath.

run   walk   hop   car   bike   bus

_____

_____

_____

_____

_____

_____

Bob saw Thin Jim jog down Fog Lane. "Running is my job," Thin Jim told Bob. "Got to stay fit and trim. I have a big race to win."

"What an odd job!" thought Bob.

"You will not get a bus at this bus stop," said Thin Jim. He thought Bob was a bit dim and wanted to help him.

"You could jog with me to the bus stop on Nut Street."

4

Bob thanked Thin Jim, but stayed where he was.

Copy out each letter in Bob's full name, Robert Cox. Write each one three times using your neatest handwriting.

 R ____ ____ ____

o ____ ____ ____

 b ____ ____ ____

 e ____ ____ ____

 r ____ ____ ____

 t ____ ____ ____

C ____ ____ ____

 o ____ ____ ____

 x ____ ____ ____

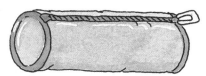

5

An hour later and Bob was still at the old bus stop. A mob of kids ran down Fog Lane, led by Bob's friend, Dot.

"We are off to see the lion cubs at the zoo," she said.
"It will be super cool.
Do you want to come too?"

Bob thanked Dot,
but stayed where he was.

Ten minutes later,
there was a **roar** like a jet plane.
A red, open-top bus came along Fog Lane.
"This is the one!" cried Bob, waving at the bus to stop.

6

Listen to the sound that the letter O makes in the middle of the words hot and Bob. Circle the words which contain that sound.

pot

cup

tug

hop

hood

goodbye

knob

cab

mop

cub

pop

cot

The red bus stopped and on Bob hopped.
"No driver," Bob thought. "How odd!"
But then the bus spoke. "I am a magic bus, so don't make a fuss.
Just hold on tight, until Mad Land is in sight."

The bus told Bob all about Mad Land.
"If the Sun gets too hot,
you may feel ill.
Just make sure you take a trip
to Sun-up Hill.
At the end of the day,
I will pick you up
at the Dot-to-Dot Shop."

BUS
STOP

Can you draw a line between the pairs of words that rhyme?

Bob   fuss

dot   cup

stop   job

bun   fog

bus   had

up   fun

dog   top

mad   got

9

Mad Land was not like any place Bob had ever seen.
The grass was blue, the water was red and the Sun was green.
A dog in a tugboat threw Bob a small cup.

"Dip the cup in the river," said the dog to Bob.

Cherry Pop River

"Take a sip of the water.
It really is tops!"
Bob dipped the cup in the river and took a sip.
It fizzed and popped in his tummy.
It felt funny, but tasted yummy.

Add the right word to each sentence, so that the sentence makes sense.

cried   Take   told   want   help   zoo

"Running is my job," Thin Jim _____ Bob.

He thought Bob was a bit dim
and wanted to _____ him.

"We are off to see the lion cubs at the _____ ,"
she said.

"Do you _____ to come too?"

"_____ a sip of the water."

"This is the one!" _____ Bob.

Bob hopped and skipped through Mad Land.
He found the big Bun of Fun.
It must have weighed a ton!

Bob walked up some steps by the Bun of Fun.
With a big jump, he landed on top of the bun.

BOING!

Bun of Fun

Bob hopped up and down on the bun. What fun!
By the time Bob got off, his face was bright red.
He felt rather hot and a little bit ill.
So he did what the bus said and went to Sun-up Hill.

All these letters have become mixed up as they jumped on the Bun of Fun. Can you write them out in alphabetical order?

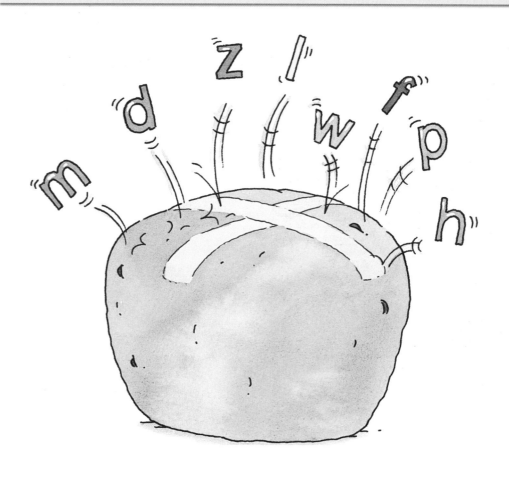

_ _ _ _ _ _ _ _ _

Bob got to the top of Sun-up Hill.
Now he felt very hot and ever so ill.

Here Bob found a very big
knob made of tin.
Around it was a dial
with numbers one to ten.

Bob jumped when the
Sun spoke to him.

"Even I am hot, Bob. Could you turn me down a bit?"
Bob turned the knob from ten to six.

"**Phew**," said the Sun. "That will do the trick!"

These mixed-up letters spell some words on the story page opposite. Can you sort them out and write the words?

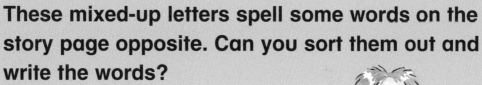

oBb _____

tho _____

otp _____

uSn _____

tbi _____

xis _____

etn _____

nit _____

B ob walked down the hill to the Dot-to-Dot Shop.
Inside was a fox wearing a spotty hat and flip-flops.
Lots of little dots floated around the shop.

"Are you hungry, young Bob?"
asked the fox.
"If you are, join the dots
to make a hot dog."

"A dot-to-dot hot dog!
Now that is **mad!**" cried Bob.

"Well, you are in Mad Land," said the fox.
Bob nodded, took a pen and jotted lines between the dots.

All these buses are missing either the letter **O** or the letter **U** from the place where they are going. Can you add the right letter or letters?

F__g Lane

S__n-__p Hill

N__t Street

B__s Station

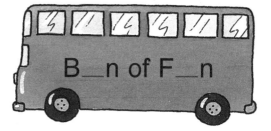

B__n of F__n

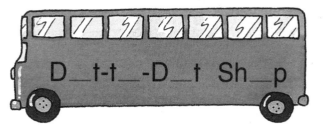

D__t-t__-D__t Sh__p

Bob joined the last dot and j^um^ped in surprise.
A big hot dog was in front of his eyes.

"Take a bite if you like," said the fox.
Bob ate the dot-to-dot hot dog
and gave his tummy a pat.
The fox said, "How **yummy** was that?"

Just then, there was a roar like a jet plane.
Outside the Dot-to-Dot Shop, the red bus pulled up again.
"Time to go home. Hop on, Bob," said the bus.

Can you match the words to these items from the Dot-to-Dot Shop? Join up the dots to help you and then write the word that matches the picture.

box   cup   jug   dog   fan   bag

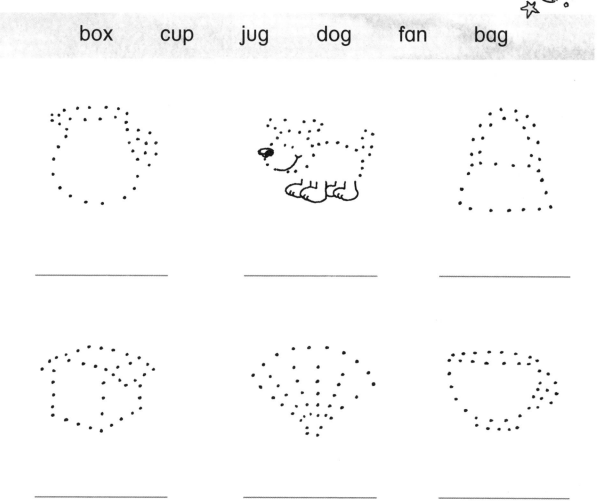

_____   _____   _____

_____   _____   _____

Bob said goodbye to the fox and hopped on the bus. He was sad to leave Mad Land, but did not make a fuss.

"Come on now, Bob," said the bus. "It is not all bad. It will be fun to go home and play with your Mum and Dad."

"I can tell them about the Bun of Fun," said Bob, with a happy nod.

"And you can visit Mad Land again with me," said the bus.

"Really, I can come back?" said Bob with a smile.

"Yes, just wait at the old bus stop, I'll pop back once in a while!"

Can you answer these questions about the story of Bus Stop Bob?

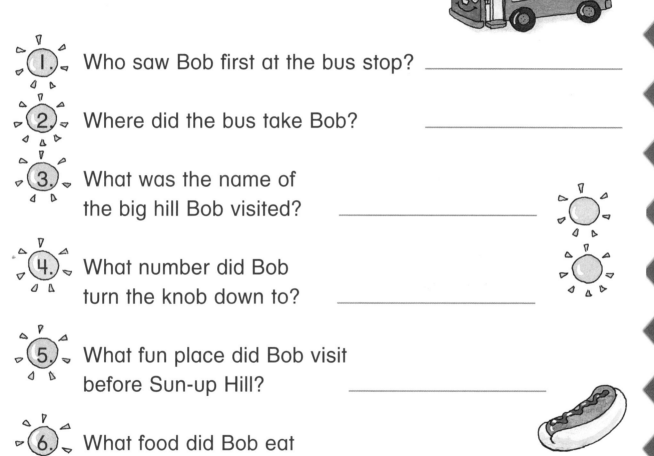

1. Who saw Bob first at the bus stop? _____

2. Where did the bus take Bob? _____

3. What was the name of the big hill Bob visited? _____

4. What number did Bob turn the knob down to? _____

5. What fun place did Bob visit before Sun-up Hill? _____

6. What food did Bob eat at the Dot-to-Dot Shop? _____

Answers

Page 3

hop

car

walk

bike

run

bus

Page 5

R R R

o o o   C C C

b b b   o o o

e e e   x x x

r r r

t t t

Page 7

pot	mop
hop	pop
knob	cot

Page 9

Bob – job	bus – fuss
dot – got	up – cup
stop – top	dog – fog
bun – fun	mad – had

Page 11

"Running is my job," Thin Jim <u>told</u> Bob. He thought Bob was a bit dim and wanted to <u>help</u> him.

"We are off to see the lion cubs at the <u>zoo</u>," she said.

"Do you <u>want</u> to come too?"

"<u>Take</u> a sip of the water."

"This is the one!" <u>cried</u> Bob.

Page 13

d f h l m p w z

Page 15

Bob
hot
top
Sun
bit
six
ten
tin

Page 17

Fog Lane
Nut Street
Bun of Fun

Sun-up Hill
Bus Station
Dot-to-Dot Shop

Page 19

jug

dog

bag

box

fan

cup

Page 21

1. Doc Box
2. Mad Land
3. Sun-up Hill
4. six
5. the Bun of Fun
6. a hot dog

Published 2005

Letts Educational, The Chiswick Centre,
414 Chiswick High Road, London W4 5TF
Tel 020 8996 3333   Fax 020 8996 8390
Email mail@lettsed.co.uk
www.letts-education.com

Text, design and illustrations © Letts Educational Ltd 2005

Book Concept, Development and Series Editor:
Helen Jacobs, Publishing Director
Author: Clive Gifford
Book Design: 2idesign ltd, Cambridge
Illustrations: Louise Gardner, The Bright Agency

Letts Educational Limited is a division of Granada Learning.
Part of Granada plc.

British Library Cataloguing in Publication Data

A CIP record for this book is available from the British Library.

ISBN 1 84315 485 4

Printed in Italy

Colour reproduction by PDQ Digital Media Solutions Ltd, Bungay,
Suffolk NR35 1BY